Roger Coote and Diana Bentley

My Grandparents

I have got four grandparents –
two grandmas and two grandads.
When they were born they were
all small babies.

They were children just
like me.

7

They played games . . .

. . . and made friends.

When they were grown up
each pair of my grandparents met . . .

. . . and fell in love . . .

. . . and got married.

13

Each pair of my grandparents
had a baby.
One baby was my mother . . .

. . . and the other baby was my father.

My mother lived with her family.

My father lived with his family.

They both grew up and one day
they met and fell in love . . .

. . . and got married . . .

. . . and had a baby – me!

Ever since then my grandparents have loved me very much.

They take me for walks . . .

. . . and read me stories.

They are sad when they have to
say goodbye . . .

27

. . . and happy when they come to visit me.
They are my grandparents and I love them too.

Notes for adults

Children who go to school already knowing how a book 'works' have a great deal of knowledge that will help them to make the entry into reading much easier. It is far more important to share a book with a child than to try to teach him/her to read. These Firefly books aim to introduce very young children to the world around them.

Before reading this book talk about the pictures on the cover. What does your child think the book is about? Talk about the title and point to the words. Tell him/her that all books are written by authors and often illustrated by a different person. Show him/her the names of the author and illustrator.

Before reading the story look through the book together and talk about the illustrations. If you wish, you can use the discussion points below, or make up your own questions. Encourage the child to tell his/her own story to the pictures. This important pre-reading skill helps children to develop an understanding of story that is essential to reading. Do let your child hold the book and give him/her time to look at the pictures before talking about them. Adults often rush in with questions far too soon.

Remember, when discussing the pictures there is no 'right' or 'wrong' guess. Accept what your child suggests and add your own ideas. You will be bringing much more knowledge to the pictures but s/he may surprise you.

After reading the book let your child explore the book on his/her own. S/he may want to return to a favourite picture, retell the story to a special toy, or just turn the pages pretending to be a reader. A joy in books comes from the reader being allowed to use them as s/he wishes and not necessarily in what an adult thinks is the 'right' way.

Discussion points

Talking about the illustrations will help your child to get more from the story. Here are some suggestions for things to discuss. The numbers refer to the pages on which the illustrations appear.

7	Have you ever seen children dressed like this? What games are they playing? What games do you like playing?
8/9	How many children can you see?
11	What are these people sitting on?
12/13	What do these old photographs show?
16	Where do you think the children are going? Will they go by car? Is it a warm day?
17	What are the boy and his mother doing?
18/19	Where are these people? What do you think they have in their bags?
23	Whose birthday is it? How many people can you count? Who is the youngest person in the picture?
27	Who is going away? Who is loading the car?
29	Who wants to ride the horse? Do you think the horse has a name?